Library of Congress Cataloging-in-Publication Data available upon request.

Luna Peak Publishing
Sierra Madre, CA | www.lunapeakpublishing.com

ISBN 978-1-7355958-8-7

FOLLOW ME, CANCER FREE

By Melody Lomboy-Lowe

Illustrations by Graciela Eastridge

Lettering by Kelly Gee

HELLO,
MY NAME IS MELODY
FOLLOW ME,
CANCER FREE

EVERY DAY
I MAKE SURE
TO HELP MY BODY
FIND A CURE

IT IS IMPORTANT TO
PLAY

IT IS IMPORTANT TO
REST

IMPORTANT TO LISTEN TO THOSE WHO KNOW BEST

DOCTORS AND NURSES
WITH EXPERT CARE
HELP ME
FIGHT THIS BATTLE
THAT ISN'T QUITE FAIR

EVERY DAY I MAKE SURE I AM READY TO FIGHT BY EATING HEALTHY AND DOING WHAT'S RIGHT

I ALSO NEED MY
FRIENDS AND FAMILY
TO HELP ME BE
CANCER FREE

SOMETIMES I HAVE TO GET
AN AWFUL SHOT,
BUT WHEN IN PAIN,
THINK A **HAPPY THOUGHT**

You and I both know it's not easy, especially on days I feel extra QUEASY

IT'S A LONG ROAD AHEAD—
IT ISN'T ALL BAD
YOU WILL BE
PROUD AND AMAZED
BY THE STRENGTH THAT
YOU HAD

SO KEEP YOUR
HEAD UP
AND BE SURE TO
STAY STRONG

EVEN WHEN YOU FEEL
LIKE EVERYTHING
IS GOING WRONG

You're a SURVIVOR
EVERY MOMENT
YOU TRY,
DON'T WASTE TIME
ON THINKING WHY

MANY HAVE WON
THE BATTLE
YOU HAVE NOW

You will look back at this time and think to yourself, "WOW!"

IF WE CAN DO THIS, WE CAN DO ANYTHING!

JUST THINK—
WHEN YOU ARE HEALTHY,
YOU WILL FEEL
AMAZING !

MY CANCER JOURNEY
IS NOW THROUGH,
IT IS NOW TIME
FOR YOU
TO SPREAD HOPE TOO!

About the Author

Melody Lomboy-Lowe was born and raised in Southern California. She is a childhood cancer survivor of leukemia and has been an advocate in the cancer community ever since. *Follow Me, Cancer Free* is a book she wishes she had at diagnosis. Her first book, *Beyond Remission: Words of Advice for Thriving*, is a book of hope that features cancer survivor portraits and stories to inspire and provide community to newly diagnosed fighters. Helping others heal and celebrate life through adversity is a mission she continues within Luna Peak Foundation which she co-founded. She enjoys being outdoors with her husband and three sons.

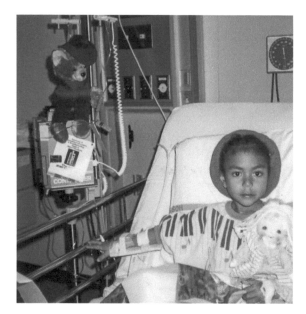

Melody age 6 with her beloved teddy bear.

Melody today, celebrating her remission since 1983.

About the Illustrator

Graciela Eastridge is an artist from Southern California, currently studying animation at the School of Visual Arts in New York. This is her debut in children's book illustration, and she had a lot of fun bringing little Melody to life! She is also a childhood cancer survivor and loves giving back to the cancer community. She enjoys playing video games and being with her family, including their dogs and bird.

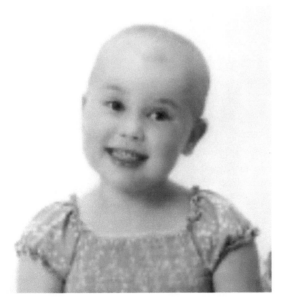

Graciela age 4 when she fought cancer.

Graciela today, celebrating her remission since 2008.

CPSIA information can be obtained
at www.ICGtesting.com
Printed in the USA
BVHW020758300821
614827BV00009B/5